THE
CONFIDENCE
JOURNAL

vie

THE CONFIDENCE JOURNAL

An Hachette UK Company
www.hachette.co.uk

Vie Books, an imprint of Summersdale Publishers Ltd
Part of Octopus Publishing Group Limited
Carmelite House
50 Victoria Embankment
LONDON
EC4Y 0DZ
UK

www.summersdale.com

Printed and bound in the Czech Republic

ISBN: 978-1-78783-305-0

Substantial discounts on bulk quantities of Summersdale books are available to corporations, professional associations and other organizations. For details contact general enquiries: +44 (0) 1243 756902 or email: enquiries@summersdale.com.

THIS JOURNAL BELONGS TO...

_____

INTRODUCTION

Confidence comes from feeling good about yourself and believing in your abilities. It's a state of mind which is conveyed to others through your voice, body language, demeanour and actions. Lack of self-confidence is characterized by critical self-talk and self-doubt, which can hold you back and prevent you from realizing your full potential. It's important to note that while confident people may doubt themselves from time to time, they don't let their fears stop them from achieving their goals. What many people don't realize is that confidence grows with use, like a muscle. Confident thinking and behaviour can be practised and, in time, it can become a habit. With the help of the following pages, providing you with useful prompts and space to explore your thoughts, you will soon learn what it is that affects your confidence, and how you can build it up to the right level for you.

Understanding
Confidence

The first step to improving your self-confidence is to understand how lack of confidence affects you and which situations in particular cause you to feel this way. It's very rare for someone to be unconfident in every area of their life. While you may lack confidence at work or among large groups of people, you may be self-assured in other areas such as cooking, playing sport or dealing with finances.

BE
TRUE
TO
YOURSELF

Keep a Confidence Diary

In order to understand your confidence issues, take some time to work out what your triggers are, and when your confidence is at its highest or lowest points. The act of writing down how you feel and what your confidence levels are like from day to day will not only help you to keep track of what may cause a bout of low confidence, but it will also be cathartic.

Remember to write down the high points as well as the lows, so that you'll have something to refer back to on low-confidence days, reminding you that things can be better.

Try to be like the turtle –
at ease in your own shell.

Bill Copeland

TENSION IS WHO YOU THINK YOU SHOULD BE.

RELAXATION IS WHO YOU ARE.

Chinese proverb

Think of Your Confident Place

Ask yourself, where do you feel most and least confident? This is not just a matter of location — although for some people certain places bolster their

confidence or make them feel worse — it is more about the areas of your life you feel are at polar opposites where your confidence is concerned.

Write down the people and places that make you feel most confident.

....

....

....

....

....

....

....

....

....

....

....

....

....

....

....

....

Change Your Thoughts

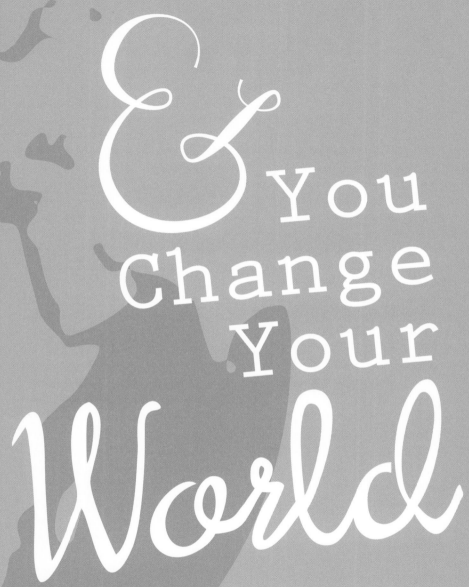

Change Your Thoughts & You Change Your World

Norman Vincent Peale

Confidence Tips

Self-doubt is the enemy of self-confidence. Use these tips to identify when you are being plagued by negative thoughts and to refresh your self-image. The tips in this section reveal how you can take back control by challenging your thoughts to build a more positive self-image.

The power of your mind

Your thoughts affect the way you feel and behave. The habit of thinking negatively about yourself can lead to low self-confidence and self-worth. However, you don't have to be at the mercy of your thinking. Remind yourself that you are in control, and you can take charge of your negative thought patterns.

Ask yourself "why?"

One of the key ways to challenge negative thoughts that drain your confidence is to ask "why?" For example, the commonly held negative thought "I'm not good enough" can make you worried about many aspects of your life; perhaps you feel you are not good enough at your job, not a good enough friend, not a good enough partner. Now is the time to ask yourself why that is: can you find

five empirical reasons why you are not good enough? It is unlikely you can. Let logic prevail; if the only way you can answer this simple question is with "because I know it's true" or with minor incidents from the past, you can begin to change your self-perception.

Would you say it to a friend?

Coming to terms with the previous tip can be particularly hard if your confidence is at an all-time low, because you may strongly believe the thought you are trying to challenge. You may even find reasons, however spurious, that it is "true". Try this: think about your best friend, sibling or colleague – somebody you respect. Now, would you tell this other person what you are telling yourself? The likelihood is that your answer is no. You may even be shocked at the thought; why would you treat someone that

way? The answer is, you already do: yourself. The lesson here is to treat yourself like your best friend. Allow yourself the same consideration you would allow another person and be kind to yourself.

Visualize a more confident you

When starting out on a journey of self-improvement, it can be hard to see what the end result will be. It is easy to become bogged down in the "what ifs" a situation brings to mind, and this is where visualization can help. Sitting in a comfortable chair, in a relaxed position, close your eyes and begin to focus on your breathing. There is no need to breathe more slowly, just pay attention to your natural breathing patterns. Next, start to build a picture in your head of how a more confident you would look and act. Notice the details and enjoy the feeling of confidence from within.

Draw This!

Once you have visualized yourself as a more confident
you, and what a positive situation might look like
for you, transfer your mental image to paper
and see it as something you can aspire to.

**Use this space to draw or describe
the scene that you pictured.**

Spring-clean your belief system. What you believe is what you become.

IT IS BEST
TO ACT WITH

CONFIDENCE,

NO MATTER HOW LITTLE
RIGHT YOU HAVE TO IT.

Lillian Hellman

Use Mantras

A mantra is a positive phrase that you repeat to yourself,
confirming your positive thoughts with affirmations, such as
"I am" and "I will". Regularly repeating your chosen mantras
(out loud, if possible, as this can make it more effective) will
help you reaffirm your faith in yourself and your abilities.

**Write your mantras here and look at
them when you need inspiration.**

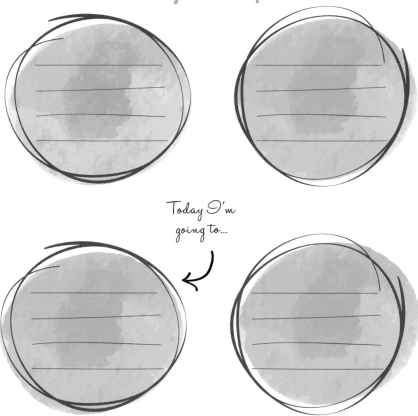

Today I'm
going to...

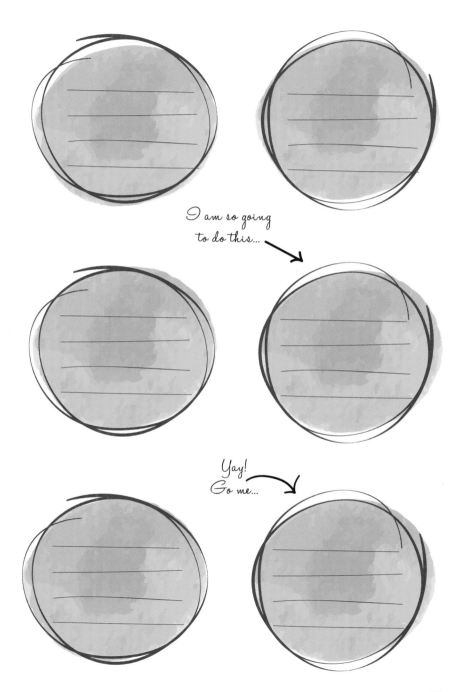

I am so going
to do this...

Yay!
Go me...

23

**WORRY PRETENDS TO BE
NECESSARY BUT SERVES
NO USEFUL PURPOSE.**

Eckhart Tolle

IF YOU FOCUS ON LIFE'S POSITIVES, THE NEGATIVES WILL FADE AWAY.

List Ten Things You Like About Yourself

Write down ten things you like about yourself. It doesn't matter how small or "silly" these things are. Maybe you make the best cup of tea, or you have a talent for making your friends laugh. Focusing on things that you like about yourself will help you to break the habit of putting yourself down. Keep adding to the list and feel your confidence soar.

Body Confidence

How you hold your body affects your state of mind. This is because your muscles are directly connected to your brain's emotional centres. Simple changes to your posture and movement can help you to feel more powerful and in control.

Straighten up

Are you slumping in your chair or slouching your shoulders when you stand? If so, straighten up! Improving your posture can instantly make you appear more positive and confident to others. Research shows it also leads to more confident thoughts and a better mood. Open your chest and keep your head level, and you'll look and feel more assured and poised.

Power pose

Two minutes standing in a "power pose" can dramatically alter your brain chemistry. Try adopting a wide stance with your hands up in the air, as if you've just won the lottery or your football team has just scored a goal. Alternatively, try the "Wonder Woman" pose, with your feet slightly apart and your hands on your hips. While you might not want to do this in the office, you can quickly do this in the toilets or when no one's about whenever you need an instant confidence boost.

Nod your head

Nodding your head not only signals "yes" to other people, it also signals "yes" to your brain. Researchers think nodding acts as a kind of self-validation, telling yourself that you have confidence in your own thoughts. The important thing to note is that this works whether the thought is positive or negative. If you nod your head while thinking negative thoughts, this can strengthen your disapproval. Nod away whenever you think positive thoughts and you'll give your confidence an extra boost.

WHATEVER
WE
EXPECT
WITH

CONFIDENCE

BECOMES

OUR

OWN

SELF-
FULFILLING

PROPHECY.

Brian Tracy

WITH CONFIDENCE, YOU HAVE WON BEFORE YOU HAVE STARTED.

Marcus Garvey

Be Assertive

When we lack confidence, it can seem like the easier option to bow to the wishes of others and say "yes" to everything, even if you are really not happy with the situation. Though it seems like the simplest option, doing this in fact negatively affects your confidence, as you are essentially telling yourself that the wishes of others are more important than your own. Being assertive doesn't have to mean being aggressive. The main thing is that you realize your own needs are as important as everybody else's.

Follow the prompts below to practise ways that you can say "no" when you need to.

I can't take that on because...

I appreciate the offer but...

I'm sorry but I can't come because...

_____
_____
_____
_____
_____

That sounds great, but...

_____
_____
_____
_____
_____
_____
_____
_____
_____
_____
_____
_____
_____
_____

Act Confident

Acting confidently can make you *feel* more confident. Even if you're feeling anxious, there are clever ways of making yourself appear more confident to others. The following tips will help you to adopt the qualities of a calm, self-assured person.

Say it like you mean it

The tone of voice you adopt when speaking to people will show whether you feel confident or not. If you speak in a way which makes it obvious to the listener that you are nervous, such as in a high-pitched, broken tone, or by speaking too quickly or quietly, they will most likely not take you very seriously. Adopting a deeper, slower, more even tone of voice shows that you feel calm and self-assured, and that you know what you are talking about. This is particularly useful when speaking in public: for example, when giving a presentation at work.

Make eye contact

People who make firm eye contact are seen as being more trustworthy and confident. However, connecting with someone's gaze can feel uncomfortable if you are shy or feeling nervous. If you struggle to look people in the eye, try fixing your gaze between the other person's eyes instead. They won't be

able to tell you're not looking them directly in the eyes and you'll give the impression of being self-assured and likeable. Just make sure you avert your gaze briefly every seven to ten seconds or so in order to avoid giving them an intimidating stare!

Fake it till you make it

Vividly imagine how your life would be if you were naturally confident right now. How would your posture be? How would you move? How would your voice sound? What would you say to yourself? What would you picture in your mind? Once you have a clear image, imagine you are this person. Step into their shoes and see the world through their eyes; feel what they feel. If you do this often, you'll forget that you're acting and confidence will become a habit.

Get comfortable being uncomfortable

Life can make you feel uncomfortable but this doesn't have to stop you from achieving your goals. In fact, if you can be comfortable with feeling uncomfortable, you'll have the confidence to handle whatever situation comes your way. Unfortunately, most of us avoid discomfort. We live within small, familiar comfort zones which limit what we do in our lives. When you regularly take risks, however, your comfort zone expands. Even taking small steps toward your goals can expand your comfort zone and make you feel more positive about life. Remember, feeling uncomfortable is usually a good sign – it means you're moving forwards and exploring new territory. You're open to new people, places, experiences and adventures in your life!

MODEL SOMEONE

One way to improve self-confidence is to model the habits of highly confident people. Find a role model who is confident in the area you'd like to improve in – whether that's giving a presentation at work or going on dates – and model as many of their behaviours, attitudes and habits as possible. If you have the chance to talk to them, ask them about their attitude and thought processes. If the person is a well-known figure, you can learn from them by reading their books or biographies, and studying their TV shows, films and interviews.

List the things that you admire about your role model here:

Make sure to include things that you can emulate. For example, you may consider your role model good-looking, but delve deeper into what makes them attractive — perhaps they have a strong sense of personal style or they are very well groomed. This will help you focus on the attributes you could incorporate into your own life to feel more confident about yourself.

Lift Yourself Up

Perfectionism — the desire to do better — can be a positive thing. But continually striving for a perceived version of perfection can stop you from being happy with who you are and from seeing all the positive things you already achieve. One of the most common perfectionist tendencies is to compare yourself with others. This may take the form of direct comparison, such

- _____
- _____
- _____
- _____
- _____
- _____
- _____
- _____
- _____
- _____

- _____
- _____
- _____
- _____
- _____
- _____
- _____
- _____
- _____
- _____

as "Max is more successful in his job than I am", or of general comparison along the lines of "I wish I could be more like Aaliyah". Either way, in seeing others as somehow better than you, you are moving your focus away from your own positives.

Every time you think that someone else is better than you, write down one of your strong points on this page. This will take your focus off other people's virtues and onto your own.

Dream lofty dreams,
and as you dream,
so you shall become.

James Allen

REMAIN *Calm* IN EVERY SITUATION BECAUSE *Peace* EQUALS **POWER.**

Joyce Meyer

Be Prepared for the Day Ahead

Feeling out of control in our busy lives can knock our confidence levels. A simple way to reduce this feeling of pressure is to plan and prepare for your working day.

At the weekend

In the morning

Pack your lunch the night before so that you are not rushing to put it together in the morning, or look up bus or train times in advance to ensure you know about any delays.

Think about a typical day in your life (for example, a weekday, if you have a regular shift pattern). Make a list under each heading of some things you could prepare in advance to make each day feel a little more under control.

The night before

First say to yourself what you would be;

and then do what you have to do.

Epictetus

Try a To-Do List

Simple as it may sound, if you are unsure about your organizational skills, then a to-do list may well be the best thing to try. Getting organized will help you to feel confident in your ability to prioritize tasks and get them done on time.

- _____
- _____
- _____
- _____
- _____
- _____
- _____

Your to-do lists can be as simple or as detailed as
you like; the main thing is that they work well for
you, and that you enjoy ticking off each task as
you complete it as an indication of achievement.

BELIEVE

IN

YOURSELF

START BY DOING WHAT'S

necessary

THEN DO WHAT'S

possible

AND SUDDENLY YOU
ARE DOING THE

impossible.

Anonymous

Draw an Opportunity Tree

It is quite possible that, even if you set the most relevant, realistic goals, you may not achieve them in the way or the time you wanted to. Life may throw something unexpected in your path, which stops you from achieving what you want, when you want. This is not failure. However, the best thing is to learn from what has happened and try again.

Think of a time or a situation that didn't go as you had hoped and write it at the bottom of the page. Draw lines branching out to things you learned or new opportunities that arose from that situation.

Big dreams often

have
small
beginnings.

Use Your Imagination

Your brain and body can't tell the difference between something you vividly imagine and something that's real. That's why your mouth waters when you imagine biting into a slice of chocolate cake. You can use this to your advantage if you're feeling nervous about doing something for the first time, such as giving a speech. By repeatedly imagining yourself wildly succeeding, you create neural

_____

_____

_____

_____

_____

_____

_____

_____

_____

_____

_____

_____

pathways in your brain which programme you to perform well the next time you give a speech in real life. In order for this to be effective, you need to run your mental movie repeatedly and you need to engage all your senses, so that the movie is as vivid and realistic as possible.

Write down a short "story" about a situation you would like to go well — remember to include all your senses!

_____

_____

_____

_____

_____

_____

_____

_____

_____

_____

_____

_____

life?

LOOK After YOURSELF

With our hectic lives, it can be easy to forget to be loving and kind to ourselves. Treating yourself as well as you would treat a best friend will give you an inner and outer glow. A soak in the bath can do wonders. As well as keeping you clean and fresh, a warm bath with your favourite bubbles or oils helps relax tense muscles and prepares the body for sleep – and being well rested boosts confidence levels. Add all the luxurious extras you desire to the bath on the opposite page: bubbles, oils, rose petals, candles, music, soaps, bath bombs, soft towels, tasty snacks or even a rubber duck!

Whatever has happened in the past, you can always take a fresh step into a future full of new hopes.

BE THE CALM
CENTRE IN
THE RAGING
FLOW OF LIFE.

Leo Babauta

Sleep Better, Feel Better

It can be hard to find motivation when you're
sleep deprived. Many aspects of our lives can fall by
the wayside, which then has a negative effect on our confidence.
Being well rested makes us feel calmer and more confident and
improves concentration, so why not give your bedtime routine a
shake-up and see what good comes of it?

Hours slept

14
13
12
11
10
9
8
7
6
5
4
3
2
1

Day of the month   1 2 3 4 5 6 7 8 9 10 11 12 13 14 15 16

Use these pages to track your sleep for a month, and make a note of how it makes you feel on the following page when you sleep less or more than usual. To fill out the chart, simply draw a line above each day, to the number of hours you slept that night.

17 18 19 20 21 22 23 24 25 26 27 28 29 30 31

Use this page to note down how you feel when you
have more or less sleep than you are used to.

_____

_____

_____

_____

_____

_____

_____

_____

_____

_____

_____

_____

_____

_____

_____

_____

_____

_____

_____

STAY IN Bed

Make a Happy List

In order to focus on the positive, try making a list of all the good things in your life. This might seem difficult at first, but you can always ask friends and family for help.

The list could be made up of personal or general points, for example "I am resilient", or "My friends are supportive".

This is something you can look back at to remind you of the good around you when negativity seems to be creeping in.

One positive thought in the morning can change your whole day.

I have two bowls of confidence for breakfast each morning.

Eric Bristow

Cherish Compliments

Receiving genuine, heartfelt compliments can boost our self-esteem — so don't brush them off. Thank the person who has complimented you and take a moment to truly internalize

what has just been said. In the same way, savour any words
of praise from family, friends and work colleagues.

Below, write the "best bits" from complimentary
emails, cards and messages, and performance
reviews at work. Read these words of praise
whenever you need a quick shot of confidence.

Nothing can dim The Light

that
Shines
from
Within

Maya Angelou

Look Good, Feel Great

Feeling good about your appearance goes more
than skin deep. Feeling happy with what you see
in the mirror each day can help you to feel more
relaxed and self-assured, which will have a knock-
on effect on your mood and confidence.

Have a good hair day

Looking after your hair is an excellent way to improve the way you feel about your body. Make sure you wash and condition as often as you need to, with products designed for your hair type: for example, dry, oily, coloured or curly hair each need different types of care. If you feel in need of a bigger boost, why not invest in a hair masque to pamper yourself with, or try out a new haircut or colour to show the new, more positive you.

Dress to impress

Does your current wardrobe leave something to be desired? Now

might be the time to replenish it with clothes which flatter you and make you feel good. The way you dress affects the way you feel, from the colours you choose to how an item fits. Choose clothes that fit well and reflect your personality. Feeling good in your clothes will make you feel more comfortable in yourself, and boost your confidence levels, both in the workplace and socially.

New for old

Revamping your wardrobe will benefit your self-esteem as you will most likely feel better about the way you look. Choose new clothes that reflect your personality as well as being suitable for your lifestyle and career. Remember, new to you doesn't have to mean brand new.

Setting yourself up with a wardrobe to be proud of can be done on a shoestring and can be great fun. Try hunting for bargains at your local charity shops, car-boot sale and on websites such as eBay and Preloved.

Colour me happy

As well as choosing the right styles and cuts, your wardrobe should be full of colours that suit your skin tone and boost your mood. Yellow is said to make you feel happier, blue is meant to calm and red is a power colour. If you are a fan of monochrome, you can still add these extra colours with accessories, such as a brightly coloured scarf, or with make-up, if you wear it.

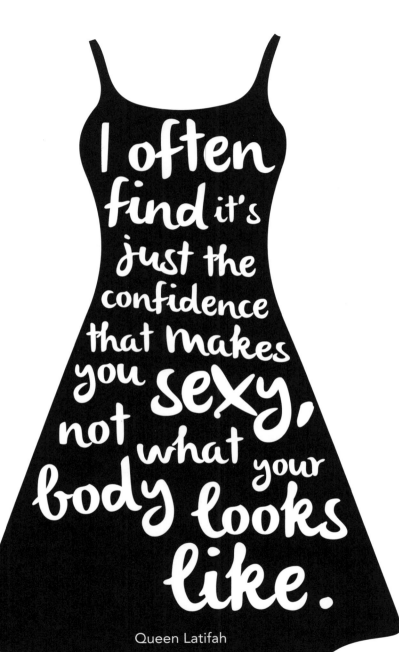

I often find it's just the confidence that makes you sexy, not what your body looks like.

Queen Latifah

BE THE BEST VERSION OF YOU

Learn Something New

Whether it's taking driving lessons, learning a new language or discovering a new hobby, mastering something new can lead to increased self-esteem. Admittedly, it takes courage to be a beginner again and acquire new skills, but the satisfaction of venturing out of our comfort zones and doing something well can make us feel good about ourselves. Is there an instrument you have always wanted to play or a sport you fancy trying? Or you might prefer to learn something practical like baking or gardening.

Write down a list of things you've always wanted to try, no matter how pie in the sky they may be, and pick one to get started.

Research shows that people who continue to learn throughout their lives are more optimistic and have a higher sense of self-worth. Plus, if you attend a class, meeting people there is a great way to enhance your social life.

YOU WERE BORN TO BE

REAL,

NOT

Perfect

The
most
Beautiful
thing you can
wear is

Confidence.

Blake Lively

Invest in Some "Me" Time

It is all too easy to believe that all your time should be spent doing "useful" things, or being there for other people. This is not always true, and trying to keep going all the time for the sake of others, without giving yourself the space to just enjoy your own company, will leave you feeling drained and tired – allowing negativity to creep in. For a positivity boost, try taking the night off. Indulge in your favourite foods, watch a film or series that you love, pick up a book you've been meaning to read and, most importantly, switch off from the rest of the world. You will likely feel all the more positive for giving your batteries a chance to recharge.

List This!

Use this page to list some activities you would like to indulge in during your "me" time. Refer back to these pages when you find yourself with some free time to remind yourself of all the things you could do to really treat yourself.

Style
is whatever
you want to
do, if you
can do it with
confidence.

George Clinton

be brave
brave
take
risks

NOTHING CAN SUBSTITUTE

experience

Paulo Coelho

Eating for Confidence

A healthy diet, which includes plenty of mood-boosting nutrients, will increase your energy and fuel your confidence from the inside out.

Eat a balanced diet

Before we look at the specific nutrients that can be beneficial to confidence, it is important to ensure you have a balanced diet. Eating the right amount of calories for your age, height and sex, and ensuring you get enough protein, fibre and vitamin-rich fruit and vegetables, while avoiding too many refined foods, will give you a good basis for general health and well-being. It should also improve digestion, which will make you feel healthier overall.

Stay hydrated

As well as being essential for good health, staying hydrated is good for your self-esteem as it helps your skin and hair look their best, which helps boost body confidence. Water also helps to flush out your system, keeping your bowels in working order and reducing feelings of bloating or puffiness. Drinking two litres of water each day is generally recommended for optimum health.

Pep up with protein

Lean proteins such as chicken, fish or tofu are a key part of a healthy diet and work as confidence boosters in several ways. Firstly, they keep you feeling fuller for longer, therefore allowing you to eat more sensibly and feel a sense of achievement at improving your diet. Secondly, their amino acids help to form neurotransmitters such as serotonin, dopamine and noradrenaline, which balance mood and keep you feeling positive. Finally, a protein-rich diet allows for quality healing and muscle building after exercise, helping you to move toward the body you want and body confidence.

Learn about good fats

When trying to eat healthily, it can be easy to see fat as the enemy. Many "healthy" products are marketed as low-fat or fat-free, and we are led to believe that fat makes you fat. This is not entirely true. Fats are an important part of your diet. They are key in neurotransmitter production due to the amino acids they contain, and unsaturated fats are important for healthy skin and hair, which in turn will make you feel more confident about yourself. As long as you get the balance right, and are eating plenty of monounsaturated and polyunsaturated fats, such as those found in avocados, olive oil and seeds, you will start to feel the benefits.

Cut Down on Caffeine

Caffeine and other similar stimulants should be avoided as much as possible. Many of us rely on that first cup of coffee in the morning to wake us up, or a cup of tea to keep us going at midday, but these caffeinated drinks could be having an adverse effect on your confidence by increasing your stress levels. Having a caffeinated drink can make us feel more alert because it induces the initial stages of the stress reaction, boosting cortisol production. Consuming

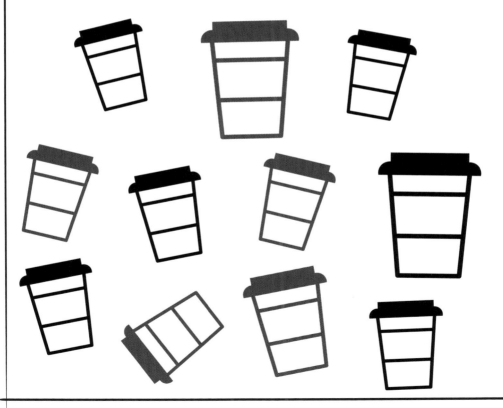

large quantities of caffeine, however, can cause the exhaustion phase of stress and lead to anxiety, which can have a very negative impact on confidence levels. Added to this, caffeine can be very addictive and stopping suddenly can cause withdrawal symptoms, which can make you feel physically unwell and emotionally under pressure – not a good combination for confidence.

Try cutting down slowly to no more than 300 mg of caffeine a day; that's the equivalent of three mugs of coffee or four mugs of tea. Colour the cups below brown for every tea or coffee you drink and bright colours for the herbal teas and decaffs you drink.

the
BEST
is
yet
to
come.

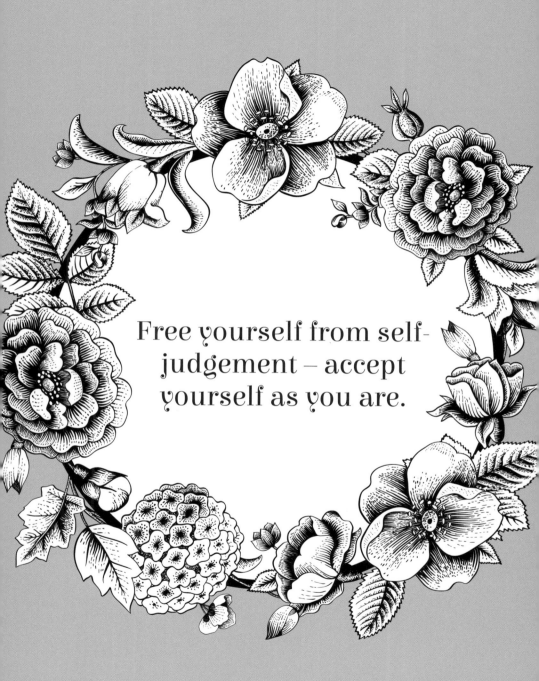

Free yourself from self-judgement – accept yourself as you are.

Be naturally Sweet

Low self-esteem can lead us to make poor food choices as we try to find comfort from food; sweet foods such as cake and chocolate offer the short-term surge of energy you may crave. Snacking on sugar-rich foods can have a very negative effect on the body both physically and emotionally; the inevitable weight gain can make you feel unhappy with your body, and has the potential to make you feel you have "given in" to certain foods. This can be a cause of stress, which in turn can lead us to reach for sugary foods again, forming a vicious cycle. Our modern lifestyles, however, mean that our stress is more likely to be because of bills we have to pay, or meetings we have to arrange, and reaching for the sugar is unhelpful because we do not really need the energy boost. Try satisfying your sweet tooth by eating naturally sweet foods such as berries, sweet potatoes, carrots and coconut.

Get a boost with B vitamins

The B-vitamin group is particularly important for maintaining a balanced mood. Among their other

functions, B vitamins are involved in the body's control of tryptophan, a building block for serotonin. Vitamin B6 is essential in the production of GABA (gamma-aminobutyric acid), which helps boost mood in a similar way to serotonin. A lack of these essential neurotransmitters can lead to low mood, which in turn can lead to very serious psychological problems. The main vitamins to pay attention to are B1, B3, B5, B6, B9 and B12, all of which can be found in a balanced diet. If you eat a lot of processed foods, or follow a vegan diet, you may be lacking in certain B vitamins, in which case adding a B-vitamin supplement to your diet can have an excellent effect on your overall health and mood.

Calm down with calcium

Calcium has a soothing, calming effect and is important in maintaining a balanced mood. It is best consumed alongside vitamin D, which also helps to enhance mood. Calcium is found in dairy foods such as milk, as well as in green leafy vegetables like kale and broccoli, lentils, beans, Brazil nuts and a wide variety of other vegetables. Fortified breakfast cereals and soya alternatives to dairy also provide a good source of calcium, and it is even found in tap water, especially in hard-water areas.

Aim for the moon. If you miss, you may hit a star.

W. Clement Stone

YOUR HEART KNOWS BEST. LISTEN TO IT.

Recipes

Use this space to write down your favourite
confidence-boosting recipes, so that you
always have some empowering and tasty food
ideas to hand when you're feeling down.

Recipes

Recipes

_____

_____

_____

_____

_____

_____

_____

_____

_____

_____

_____

_____

_____

_____

_____

_____

_____

_____

_____

_____

Recipes

WATCH YOUR ALCOHOL INTAKE

When feeling low, for example after a hard day at work, or when lacking confidence in a social situation, many people will reach for a drink to help them relax. Alcohol does have an instantly calming effect, but this is negated by the depressant qualities of alcohol, and the feeling of anxiety that can be left behind once the effects wear off. Alcohol can also disturb your sleep, contrary to the popular idea of a "nightcap". Try to cut down your drinking as much as possible, and if you do go for a tipple, opt for a small glass of Chianti, Merlot or Cabernet Sauvignon, as the plant chemicals called procyanidins which are abundant in these particular wines are beneficial to health, especially cardiovascular health. These wines are also rich in melatonin, the sleep hormone, and a well-rested person is more likely to be a confident person.

Take an average week and fill in the chart below to help you plot out your approximate alcohol intake.

When you start writing it down and working out the units it can be a bit of a shock. However, taking stock of what you're really drinking will help you realize where you could cut down a little, and feel all the positive benefits of a less-boozy lifestyle.

Day of the week	Alcohol (Y/N)	Type of alcohol	Amount	Units (approx.)
Monday				
Tuesday				
Wednesday				
Thursday				
Friday				
Saturday				
Sunday				

KNOW YOUR UNITS

Men and women are advised not to drink more than 14 units a week on a regular basis.

Shot of spirits: ~1 unit

Alcopop: ~1.5 units

Small glass of wine: ~1.5 units

Bottle of lager/cider/beer: ~1.7 units

Can of lager/cider/beer: ~2 units

Medium glass of wine: ~2.1 units

Large glass of wine: ~3 units

INACTION BREEDS
DOUBT AND FEAR.

*Action breeds
confidence
and courage.*

Dale Carnegie

SO THE PIE ISN'T PERFECT?

CUT IT INTO WEDGES.
STAY IN CONTROL
AND NEVER PANIC.

Martha Stewart

Exercising Your Way to Confidence

Exercise is an important tool for building confidence. As well as toning your muscles, regular exercise will reduce stress and help you to feel more comfortable in your own skin. Whether you join a gym or walk in a park, moving your body will give you a sense of accomplishment and a more positive body image.

Swim toward a more confident you

Swimming is one of the most effective forms of exercise, both in terms of giving you a full body workout and in allowing you to relax and unwind. The rhythmic lap of the water with each stroke, and the focus on your technique and breathing, really make this a great way to move your mind away from your worries, allowing some quality time to yourself. This alone time can give you a chance to reflect on the positive changes you are making. Add to that the fact that floating in water is a wonderfully soothing experience, and all part and parcel of a trip to the pool, and you've got a perfect recipe for confidence-boosting relaxation.

Yoga for inner and outer strength

The ancient practice of yoga is not just about bending your body, but also about bringing balance to your mind. Yoga is practised at your own pace, allowing you to take time to really understand what your body can do. It can help with confidence because of the strengthening and toning effect it has on the body, and because of the calming effect it has on the mind. Most classes will finish with yogic sleep, or guided meditation, which can leave you feeling refreshed, happier and more in touch with yourself. If you would rather not attend a class, yoga can be practised at home with the help of books, DVDs or online demonstrations.

Dance yourself fit and happy

Dancing is, for many people, one of the most fun ways to get fit, and alongside releasing the mood-boosting endorphins exercise provides, it's a great positivity cocktail. It can be as simple as putting on your favourite music at home and dancing around your living room or bedroom, or you could try a class. Jive, jazz, ballroom and Latin dance classes are all great ways to get fit and meet new people, and fitness fusion classes such as Zumba are becoming ever-more popular. Choose a style that suits you and, above all, enjoy it.

Turn
"I CAN'T"
into
"I CAN".

Never apologize for being you.

Set Your Targets

Once you've gathered some ideas about what kind of exercise you might like to take up, try setting yourself some small and achievable milestones to work toward.

Milestones	Start Date	Deadline	Date Achieved

Remember that it isn't about competing with those around you, but about celebrating your own victories and encouraging yourself to be the best you can be.

Use the space on these pages to set out your realistic milestones which will help you track your progress, as well as help you to stay motivated along the way.

Milestones	Start Date	Deadline	Date Achieved

AS IS OUR CONFIDENCE, SO IS OUR CAPACITY.

William Hazlitt

WE GAIN STRENGTH, AND COURAGE, AND CONFIDENCE BY EACH EXPERIENCE IN WHICH WE STOP TO LOOK FEAR IN THE FACE.

Eleanor Roosevelt

"Green" Exercise for a Natural Boost

"Green" exercise is any physical activity you take part in outside, in natural surroundings. Enjoy what the

_____

_____

_____

_____

_____

_____

_____

_____

_____

_____

_____

_____

_____

_____

_____

_____

great outdoors has to offer by spending more time in your garden, local park or woods. Being in natural surroundings can bring a real sense of tranquillity.

_____

_____

_____

_____

_____

_____

_____

_____

_____

_____

Exercising outdoors, be it on the coast, through fields or even in the canopy of a tree-lined road, can improve your mood, ease muscle tension and lower blood pressure. Feeling close to nature may give you the boost you need to keep calm under pressure, and feel balanced and content.

WHEN FACED WITH AN UPHILL STRUGGLE,

Relaxing

Daily life can sometimes feel like an endless, exhausting to-do list. If your stress levels are rising and you're feeling overwhelmed, take a few moments to relax. Don't think of it as wasting time because the actions you take to help your mental health are never a waste of time. Reducing your anxiety will help you to feel more confident and in control.

Colour in the image on the opposite page. Focus entirely on the act of colouring and let go of stressful thoughts and anxieties for the moment.

Remain **calm, serene,** always in control of **yourself.** You will then find out how easy it is to **get along.**

Paramahansa Yogananda

INSECURITIES ARE LOUD.

CONFIDENCE IS SILENT.

Write Away Your Worries

Everyone will have periods of worry at some point — family,
finances, career and health can all be sources of anxiety.

Not being able to "switch off" and continuing to worry about several different things at once can make us feel out of control and knock our confidence.

Write down these worries below. This allows you to voice them, helping you to think more clearly and allowing you to relax more easily.

....
....
....
....
....
....
....

....
....
....

....
....
....
....
....
....

A wise man makes his own decisions; an ignorant man follows public opinion.

Chinese proverb

THERE IS NO ONE WHO CAN TELL YOU WHO TO BE...

except yourself.

Keep it Simple

Having too many things going on around you at once can be a major cause of stress, and can give your confidence a knock, particularly if you feel like you cannot get through all the tasks ahead of you. Decluttering, throwing out old items that are no longer of use and giving them to a

charity shop or using sites such as Freecycle and eBay
is a great first step to simplifying your life, leaving you
feeling more in control, less stressed and more confident
in your ability to look after yourself and your home.

Giving away things you like or that have sentimental
value can be a bit of a wrench. Take a photo
of the things you give away and stick it in this
spread. This is a simpler way to remember the
things you love but are ready to let go of.

Talk to Someone

If you think stresses and worries are affecting your confidence, talking to someone close to you can be a huge help. Vocalizing your concerns, and hearing the reassurance and advice of someone whose opinions you trust, can alleviate anxiety and let us see that we are not alone. If you do not have someone to confide in, a counsellor or a service such as the Samaritans can provide the sympathetic ear you seek. The simple act of picking up the phone to talk to someone takes faith and demonstrates that you can be a confident, open person.

Words can fail us at the crucial moment. Write your worries or fears as bullet points on these pages and refer to them during your conversation. Planning ahead of time will allow you to be clear on what you want to say and how you want to say it.

ONCE A BELIEF BECOMES A DEEP CONVICTION, THINGS BEGIN TO HAPPEN.

Life is not easy for any
of us. But what of that?
We must have perseverance
and, above all, confidence
in ourselves. We must
believe that we are gifted
for something and that this
thing must be attained.

Marie Curie

Avoid "Catching" Stress from Your Colleagues

For many, the workplace is the most stressful area of their lives. A large amount of workplace stress is so-called "second-hand" stress. When a colleague is feeling stressed you can unconsciously absorb their feelings of negativity. To avoid this, if a colleague is talking about work or personal problems, try to say something positive about the subject or offer them some advice. To end the conversation, perhaps suggest that you are going to make a hot drink, or, if you cannot extricate yourself, make sure you stay positive and try your best not to adopt your colleague's mindset.

Writing down the things you enjoy at work will help you keep your colleagues' worries separate from your own feelings about your workplace. Jot down three things you enjoyed about work as soon as you get home to help shake off your negativity "hangover".

Keep Spending Sensible

Financial worries are one of today's biggest stressors, with more and more people in debt and/or out of work. Taking control of your finances is a great confidence boost as it helps reduce the stress that can bring your confidence levels down, and it shows that you can take a situation on and improve it. Thankfully, there are some simple ways to cut back on non-essential spending. Write a list of your financial commitments and cancel any direct debits for services you do not want or need. Cut them out of your life. Next, write a list of the things that make you happiest, such as your weekly night out with friends. Focus on putting the money that you can spare in to the things that make you happiest, rather than in empty commitments and subscriptions.

YOU HAVE TO HAVE
CONFIDENCE IN
YOUR ABILITY,

AND THEN BE TOUGH ENOUGH
TO FOLLOW THROUGH.

Rosalynn Carter

Take a

chance.

The greatest

regrets

are

opportunities

missed.

Progressive Relaxation

Just like meditation and yoga, progressive relaxation is an excellent sleep aid. It is often the case that when low mood strikes and our confidence has dipped, we lie awake at night unable to relax. The following exercise removes the pressure, breaking relaxation down into smaller steps.

Start at your feet and work your way up your body, concentrating on one body part at a time. For each body part, clench it as tightly as you can before letting it go, feeling the physical relaxation that comes with this release. Some people find it helpful to use a verbal aid, for example by saying or thinking, "I am relaxing my feet; my feet are now completely relaxed", and repeating for each body part.

Draw a rough outline of your body below and colour in the areas you will be tensing and relaxing. Pick a different colour for each area. When you practise your progressive relaxation, picture each body part glowing a different colour as you release and relax it.

Visualize Your Self-Confidence

Until you can recognize yourself as the confident, wonderful person you are, visualize your self-confidence as a separate creature. Think of it as a mascot that

you take out with you and who acts on your behalf.
Perhaps you feel too scared to approach a shop
assistant for help, but your self-confidence doesn't.

Draw your self-confidence as a creature below.

Keep your
head up
and your
heart open.

Health

IS THE GREATEST

possession.

Contentment

IS THE GREATEST

treasure.

Confidence

IS THE GREATEST

friend.

Lao Tzu

AND FINALLY...
SEEKING MEDICAL
ADVICE

We hope you enjoy the journey toward a new, more confident you! If your confidence issues are having a negative effect on your day-to-day life, it is worth speaking to your doctor about it. Although complementary therapies can help a great deal, some situations need a firmer hand and sometimes low self-confidence is a sign of more serious issues. It may be that your doctor recommends a talking therapy such as CBT (cognitive behavioural therapy), or medication, to help you get to a better place. Remember, the doctor is there to help you, not to judge; tell them everything and that way they will be able to give you the best possible advice.

Notes

Use the following notes and doodle
pages however you please!

Doodles

Notes

Doodles

Notes

Doodles

Image Credits

If you're interested in finding out more about our books,
find us on Facebook at **Summersdale Publishers**,
follow us on Twitter at **@Summersdale** and follow
our Instagram **@summersdalepublishers**.

Thanks very much for buying this Summersdale book.

www.summersdale.com